EASIEST 5-FI... PIANO COLLE...

Showtunes

15 popular showtunes arranged for 5-finger piano

Wise Publications
part of The Music Sales Group
London / New York / Paris / Sydney / Copenhagen / Berlin / Madrid / Tokyo

ANY DREAM WILL DO

Music by Andrew Lloyd Webber. Lyrics by Tim Rice.

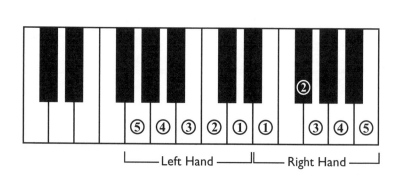

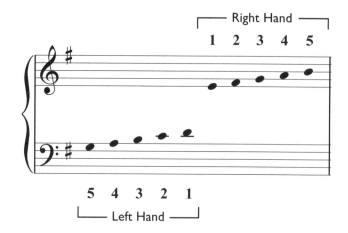

Steadily ♩ = 96

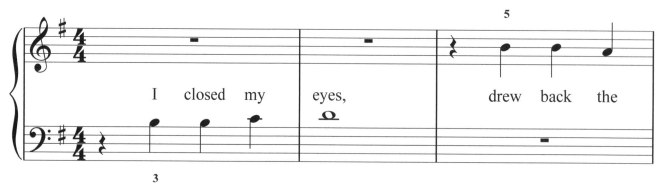

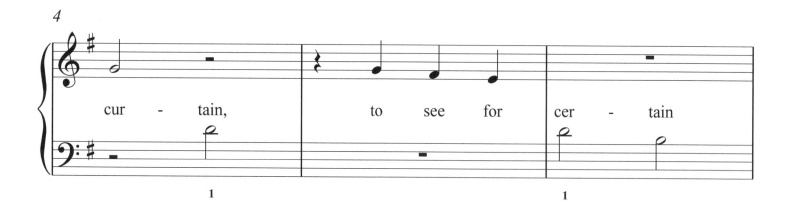

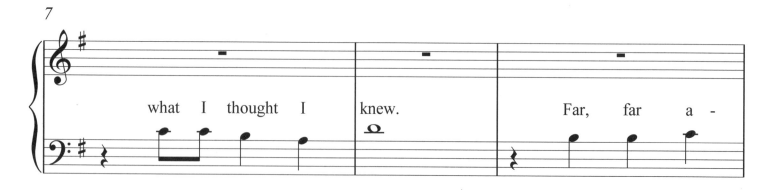

-way,   some - one   was   weep   -   ing,

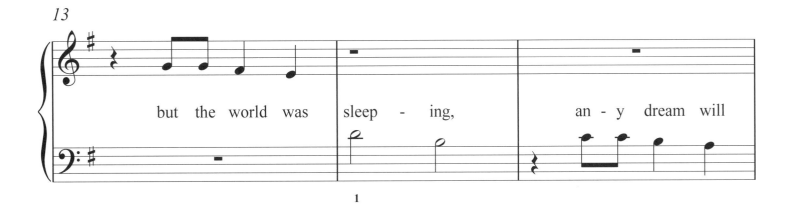

but the world was   sleep   -   ing,   an - y dream will

do,   an - y   dream   will   do,

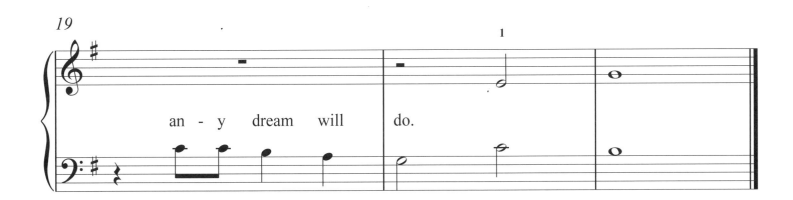

an - y   dream will   do.

MY FAVOURITE THINGS

Words by Oscar Hammerstein II. Music by Richard Rodgers.

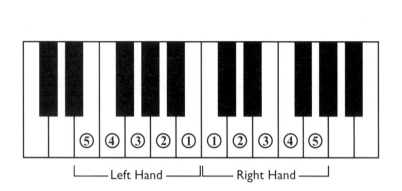

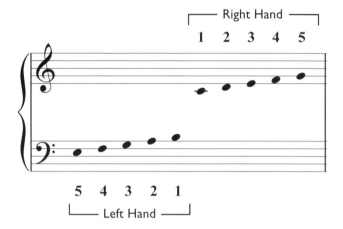

Brightly ♩ = 144

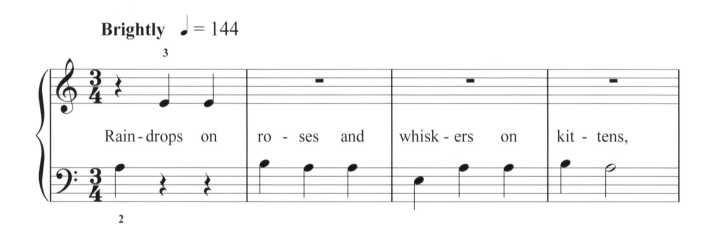

Rain-drops on ro-ses and whisk-ers on kit-tens,

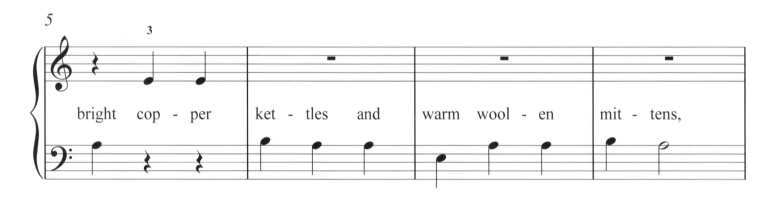

bright cop-per ket-tles and warm wool-en mit-tens,

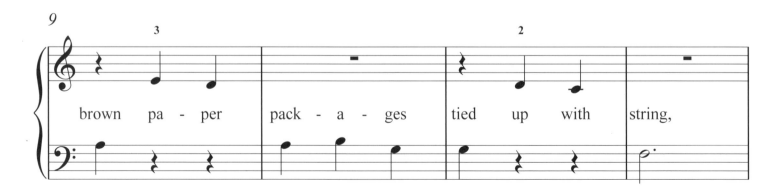

brown pa-per pack-a-ges tied up with string,

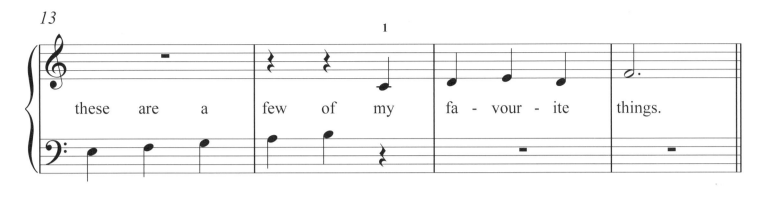

13 these are a few of my fa - vour - ite things.

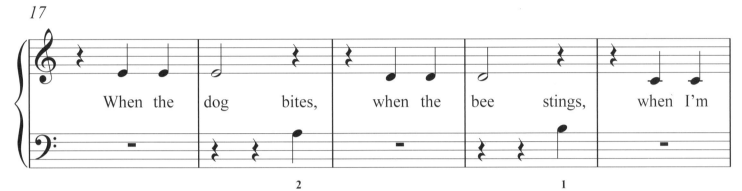

17 When the dog bites, when the bee stings, when I'm

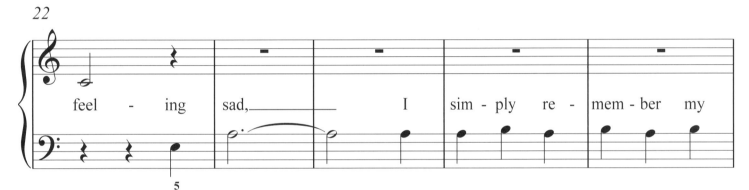

22 feel - ing sad,_____ I sim - ply re - mem - ber my

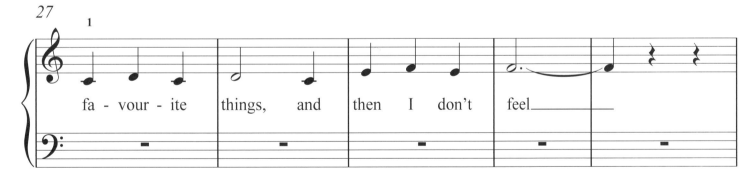

27 fa - vour - ite things, and then I don't feel_____

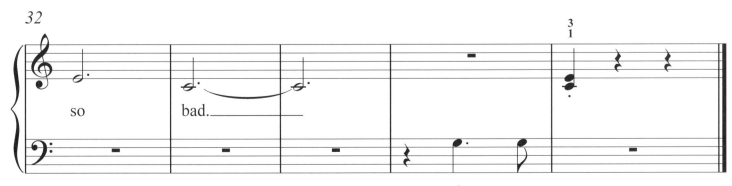

32 so bad._____

NO MATTER WHAT

Music by Andrew Lloyd Webber. Lyrics by Jim Steinman.

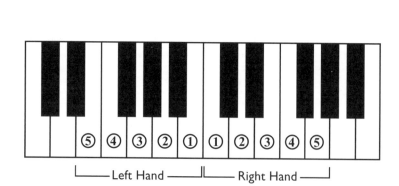

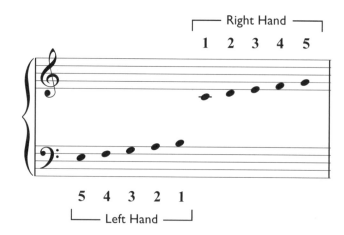

Smoothly and with confidence ♩ = 96

No mat-ter what they tell us, no mat-ter what they

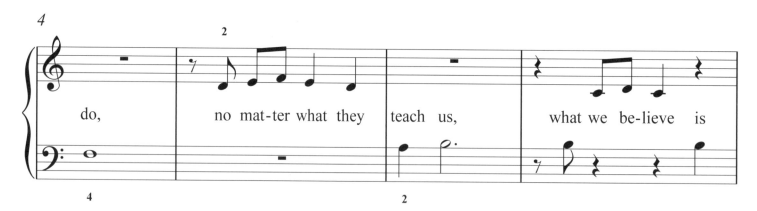

do, no mat-ter what they teach us, what we be-lieve is

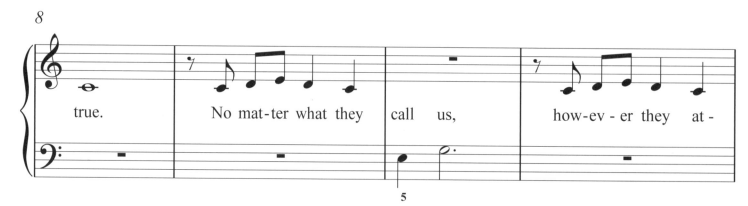

true. No mat-ter what they call us, how-ev-er they at-

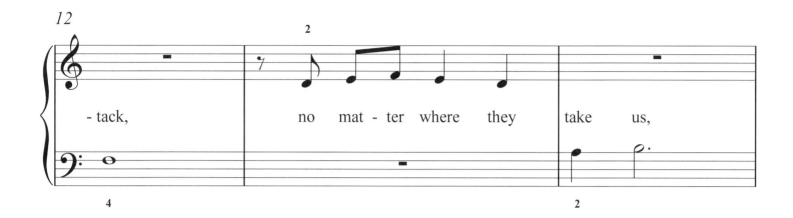

-tack,   no mat - ter where they   take   us,

we'll find our own way   back.   I   can't de - ny___   what

I   be - lieve,___   I   can't be___ what I'm   not;

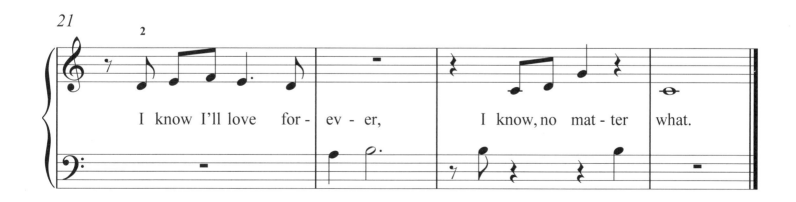

I know I'll love for - ev - er,   I know, no mat - ter   what.

BEAUTY AND THE BEAST

Music by Alan Menken. Words by Howard Ashman.

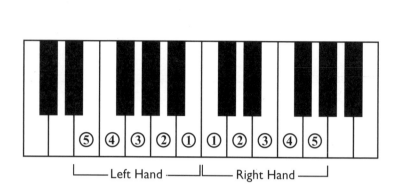

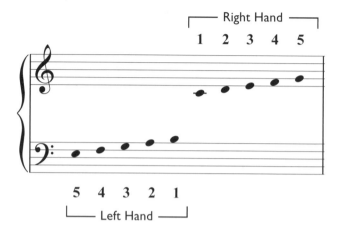

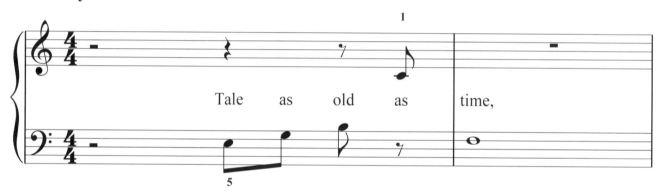

Tale as old as time,

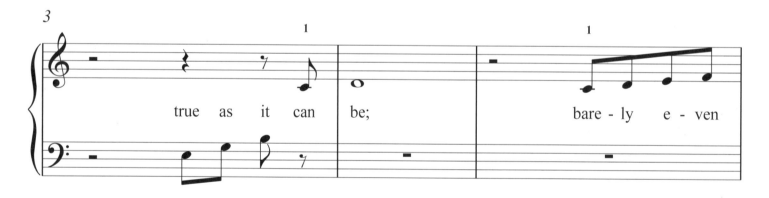

true as it can be; barely even

friends, then some-bod-y bends, un-ex-pec-ted-ly.

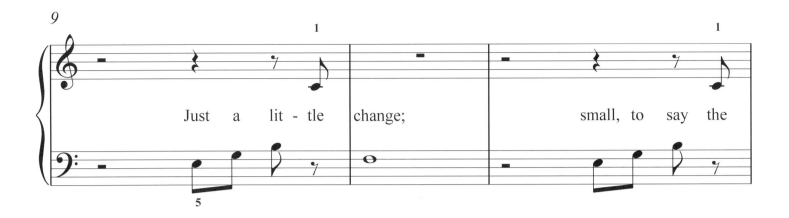

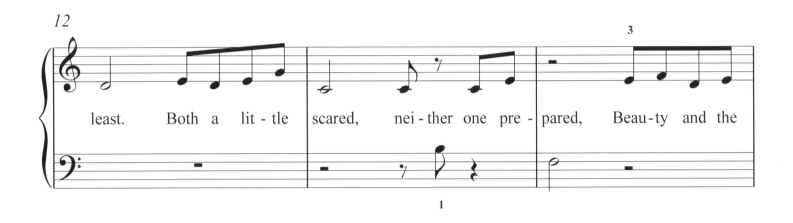

FEED THE BIRDS

Words & Music by Richard M. Sherman & Robert B. Sherman

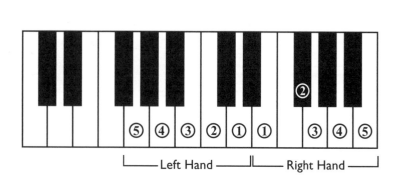

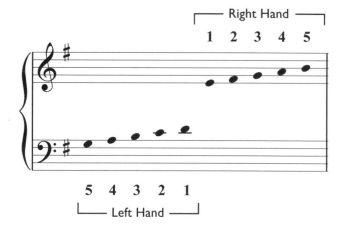

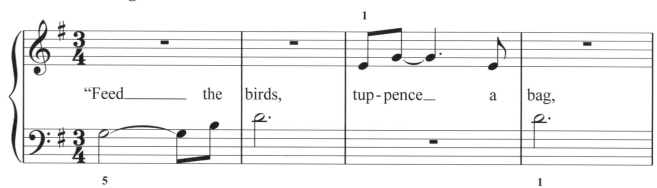

Flowing ♩ = 104

"Feed_____ the birds, tup-pence___ a bag,

tup - pence,___ tup - pence,___ tup - pence___ a bag.

Feed_____ the birds," that's what she cries, while o - ver-

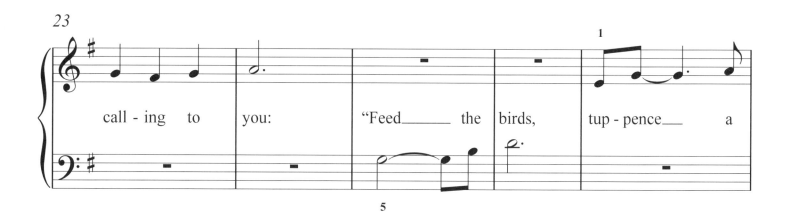

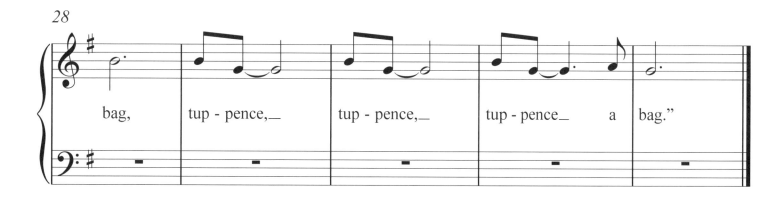

DON'T CRY FOR ME ARGENTINA

Music by Andrew Lloyd Webber. Words by Tim Rice.

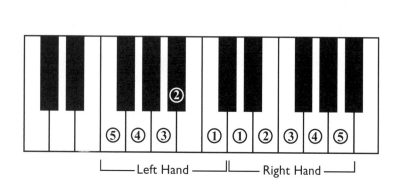

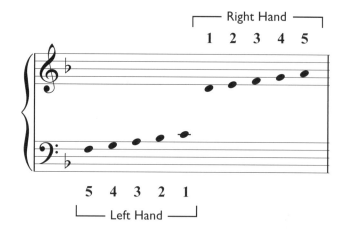

Slowly ♩ = 72

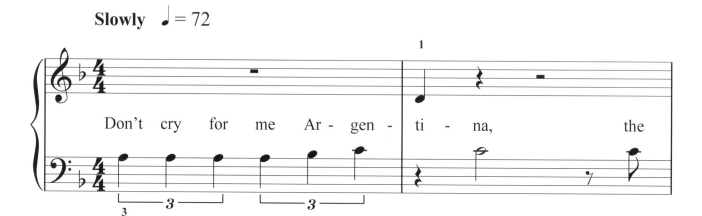

Don't cry for me Ar- gen - ti - na, the

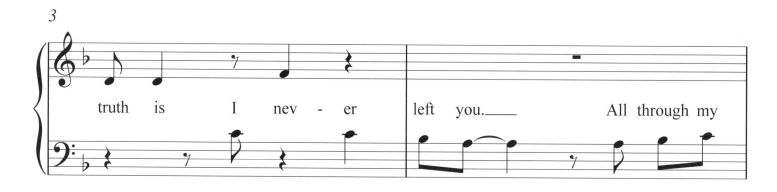

truth is I nev - er left you.___ All through my

wild days, my mad ex- is- tence, I kept my prom- ise,___ don't keep your

dis - tance.__   Have I said too much? There's   noth-ing more I can think of   to

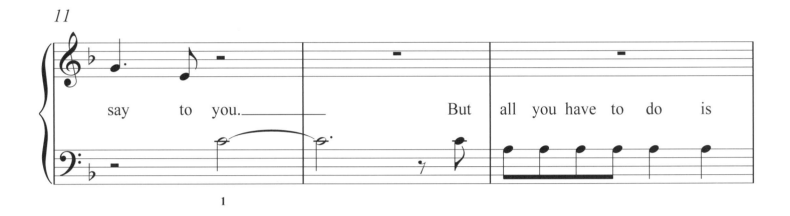

say   to   you.__   But   all   you have to   do   is

look   at   me   to   know   that   ev - 'ry   word   is   true.

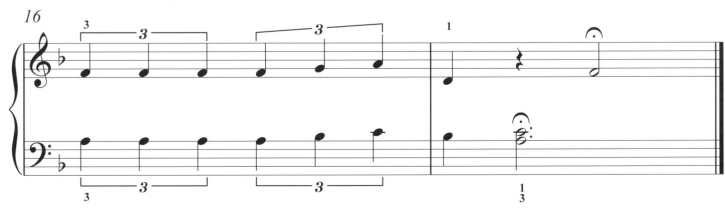

CIRCLE OF LIFE

Music by Elton John. Words by Tim Rice.

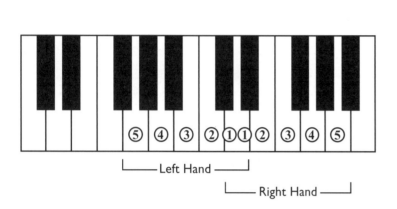

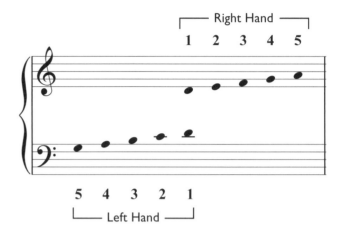

Powerfully ♩ = 100

From the day we ar - rive__ on the plan - et, and

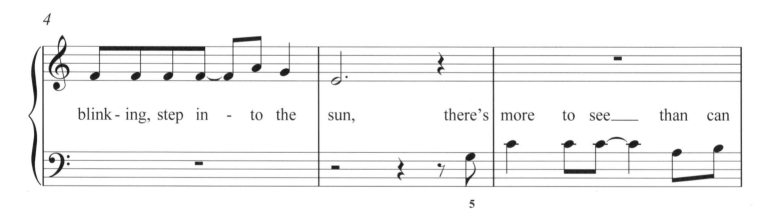

blink - ing, step in - to the sun, there's more to see__ than can

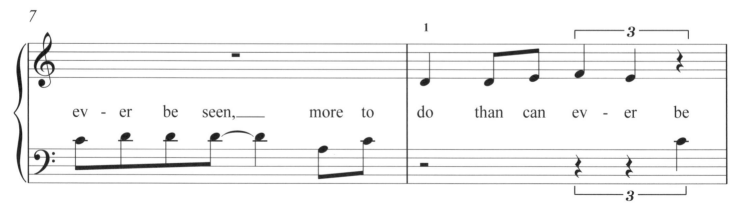

ev - er be seen,__ more to do than can ev - er be

I'D DO ANYTHING

Words & Music by Lionel Bart

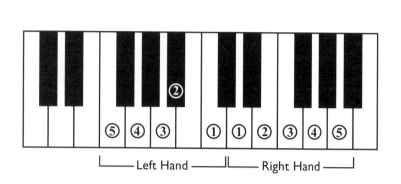

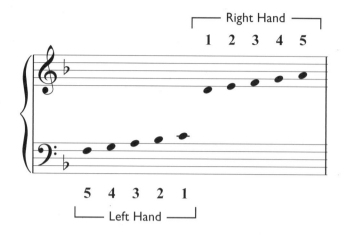

Sprightly ♩ = 144

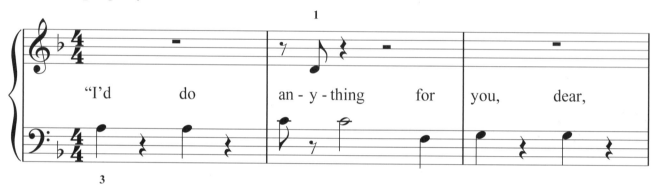

"I'd do an-y-thing for you, dear, an-y-thing, for you mean ev'ry-thing to me. I know that

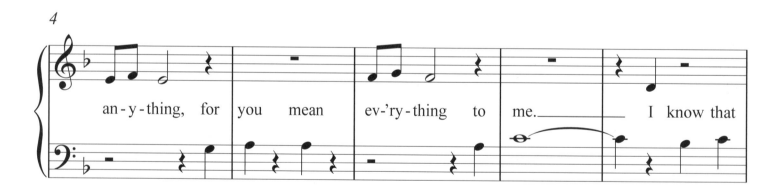

I'd go an-y-where for your smile, an-y-where, for

MAMMA MIA

Words & Music by Benny Andersson, Stig Anderson & Björn Ulvaeus

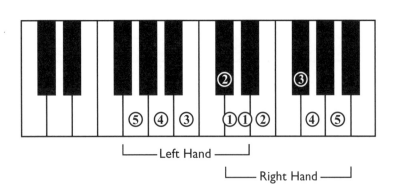

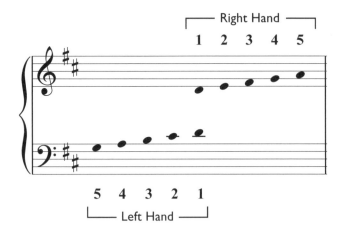

Energetically ♩ = 120

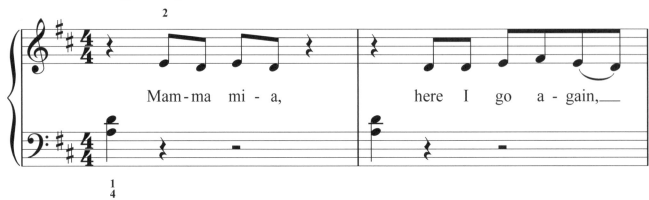

Mam-ma mi - a, here I go a - gain,

my, my, how can I re-sist you? Mam-ma mi - a,

does it show a - gain, my, my, just how much I've missed you?

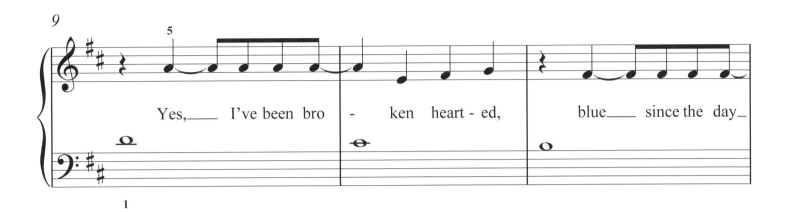

HAPPY TALK

Words by Oscar Hammerstein II. Music by Richard Rodgers.

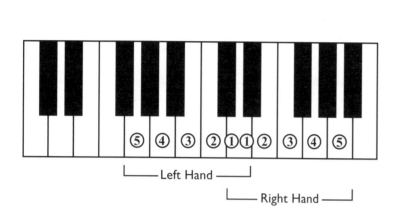

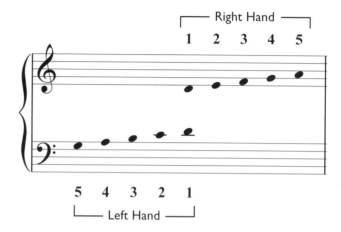

Brightly, with a bounce ♩ = 80

Hap - py talk, keep talk - in' hap - py talk,

talk a - bout things you'd like to do. You got - ta have a dream, if

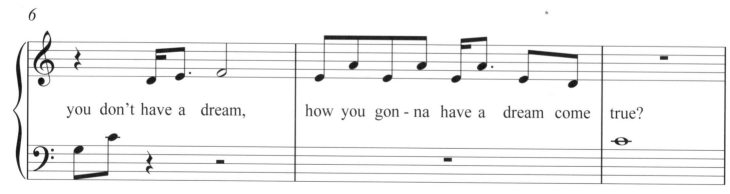

you don't have a dream, how you gon - na have a dream come true?

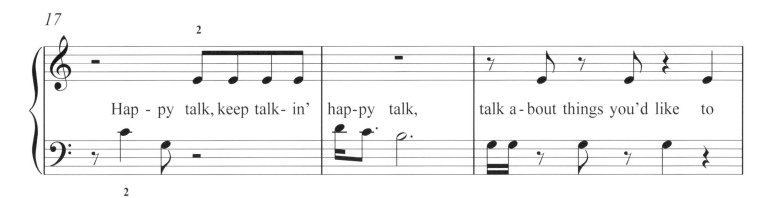

THE LAMBETH WALK

Words by Douglas Furber & Arthur Rose. Music by Noel Gay.

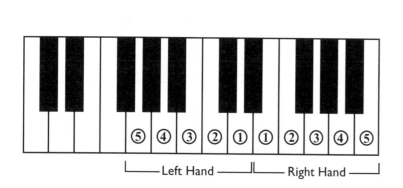

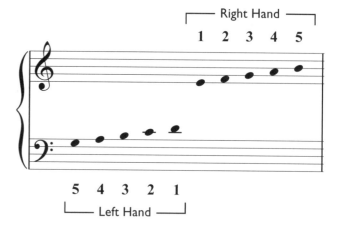

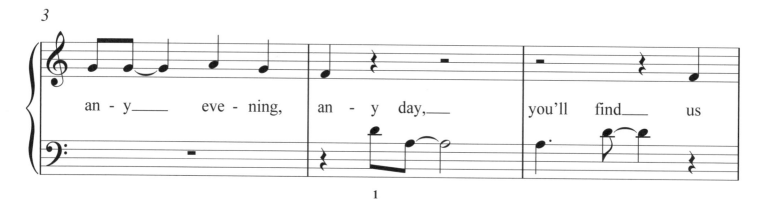

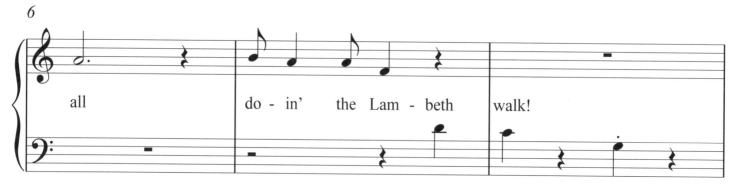

MATCHMAKER

Words by Sheldon Harnick. Music by Jerry Bock.

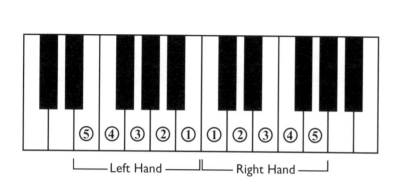

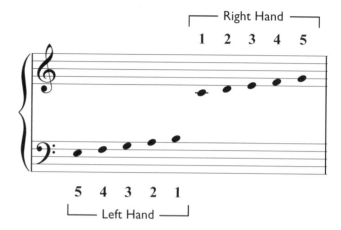

Smoothly ♩ = 168

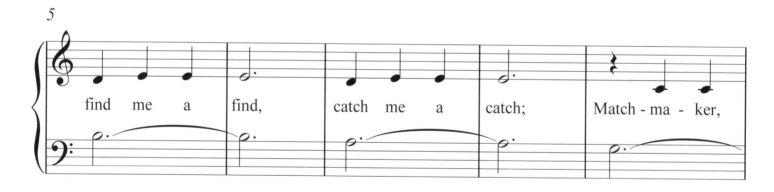

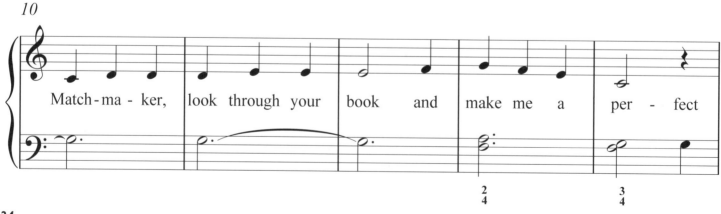

THE MUSIC OF THE NIGHT

Music by Andrew Lloyd Webber. Lyrics by Charles Hart. Additional Lyrics by Richard Stilgoe.

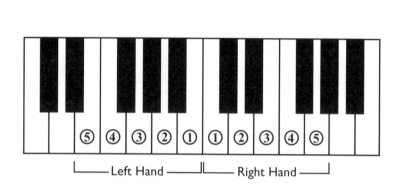

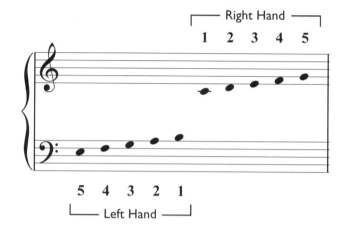

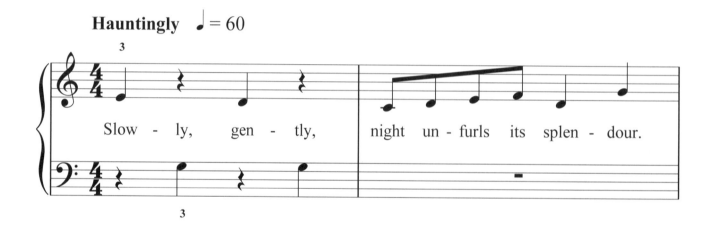

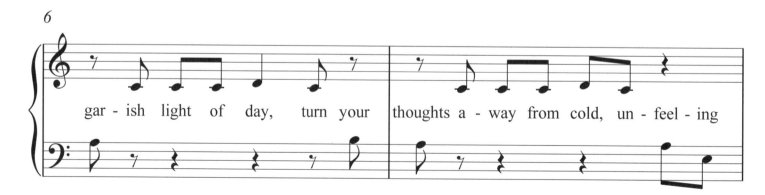

TELL ME IT'S NOT TRUE

Words & Music by Willy Russell

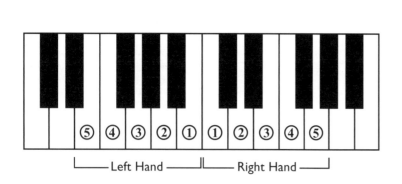

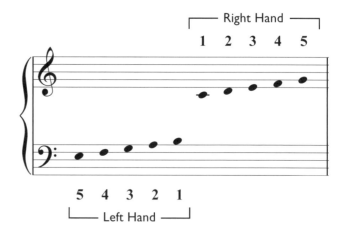

Slowly and sadly ♩ = 76

Tell me it's not true, say it's just a

stor - y, some - thing on the news.

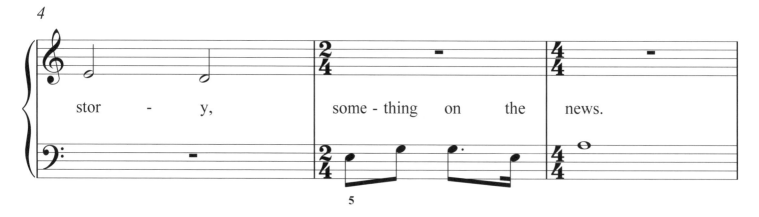

Tell me it's not true, though it's here be -

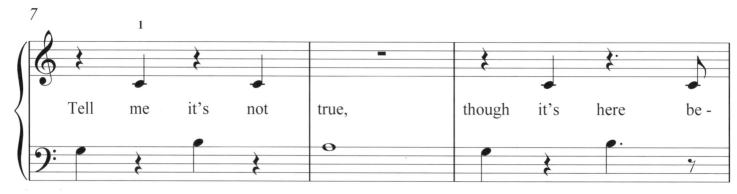

-fore me; say it's just a dream, say it's just a scene_____

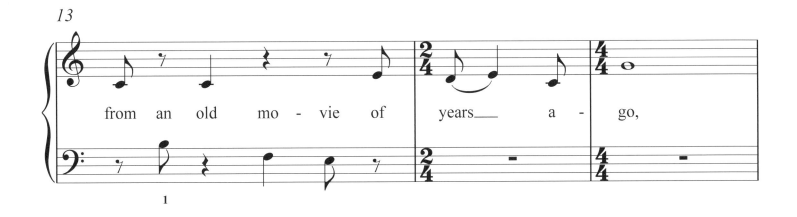

from an old mo - vie of years_____ a - go,

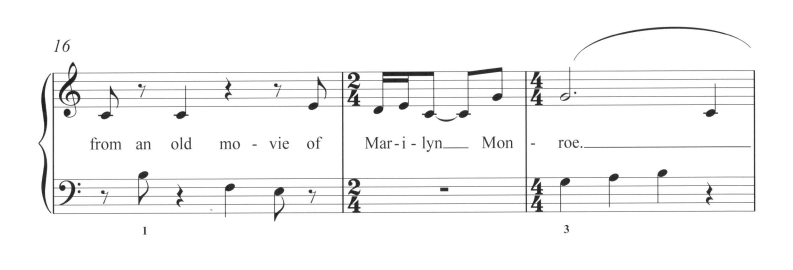

from an old mo - vie of Mar - i - lyn_____ Mon - roe._____

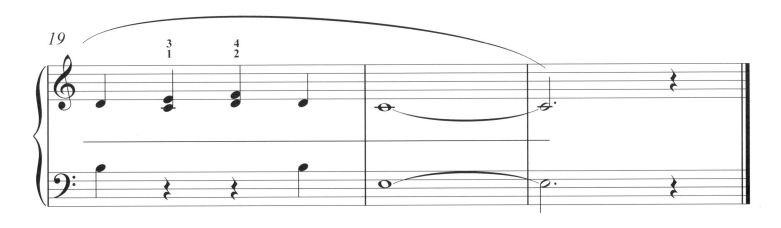

ON MY OWN

Music by Claude-Michel Schönberg. Original Lyrics by Alain Boublil & Jean-Marc Natel.
English Lyrics by Herbert Kretzmer, Trevor Nunn & John Caird.

© Copyright (Music & Lyrics) 1980 Editions Musicales Alain Boublil.
English Lyrics © Copyright 1985 Alain Boublil Music Limited (ASCAP).
All Rights Reserved. International Copyright Secured.

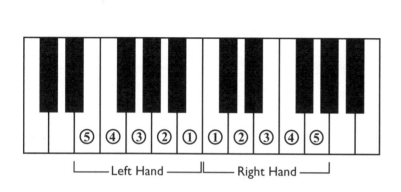

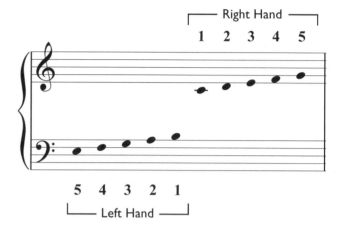

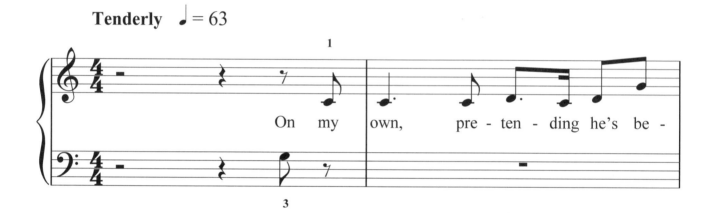

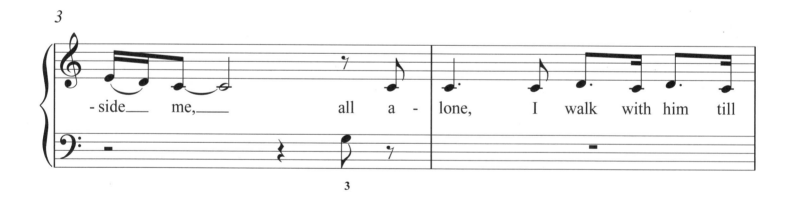

5 12 183192

EASIEST 5-FINGER PIANO COLLECTION

ALSO AVAILABLE IN THE SERIES!

Ballads
A superb collection of 15 well-known ballads, including 'Fix You', 'I Have A Dream', 'Let It Be' and 'What A Wonderful World'.
AM995346

Chart Hits
15 popular chart hits including 'About You Now', 'Bleeding Love', 'Clocks', 'Foundations', 'Shine' and 'Umbrella'.
AM995357

Film Songs
15 great film songs including 'Breaking Free', 'Don't Worry, Be Happy', 'Somewhere Out There' and 'You've Got A Friend In Me'.
AM995335

Download to your computer a set of piano accompaniments for this *Showtunes* edition
(to be played by a teacher/parent).
Visit: **www.hybridpublications.com**
Registration is free and easy.

Your registration code is RK986

Published by
Wise Publications
14-15 Berners Street,
London W1T 3LJ, UK.

Exclusive Distributors:
Music Sales Limited
Distribution Centre, Newmarket Road,
Bury St Edmunds, Suffolk IP33 3YB, UK.
Music Sales Pty Limited
20 Resolution Drive, Caringbah,
NSW 2229, Australia.

Order No. AM995324
ISBN 978-1-84772-724-4

Edited by Fiona Bolton.
Arranging and engraving supplied by Camden Music.

Printed in the EU.

Your Guarantee of Quality
As publishers, we strive to produce every book to the highest commercial standards. This book has been carefully designed to minimise awkward page turns and to make playing from it a real pleasure. Particular care has been given to specifying acid-free, neutral-sized paper made from pulps which have not been elemental chlorine bleached. This pulp is from farmed sustainable forests and was produced with special regard for the environment. Throughout, the printing and binding have been planned to ensure a sturdy, attractive publication which should give years of enjoyment. If your copy fails to meet our high standards, please inform us and we will gladly replace it.

www.musicsales.com